When I'm Feeling
Loved

Written and illustrated by Trace Moroney

The Five Mile Press

When I'm feeling loved
I feel like I could grow wings
and fly high up in the sky
amongst the stars.

When I'm feeling loved
I feel warm and safe and protected . . .
like being wrapped up in clouds
of cotton wool.

Feeling loved makes me feel

special

Some things that make me
feel loved are . . .
when a friend puts
their arm around me
and says "Thank you
for being a good friend" . . .

or, when my dog Poppy
licks my face . . .

or, when Mom or Dad tucks me
into bed at night and says,
"I love you my little snuggle-bunny."

Feeling loved makes me feel strong . . .
so when something difficult happens
I feel more confident to try to work it out by myself.

When I'm feeling loved
I feel more happy and more confident
with the person that I am.

Being loved teaches me how
to love others . . . and myself.

Love is so easy to share!

I LOVE being loved!
Do you?